Abandoned Guilt
and Absorbed Gladness

My 4,718-day IVF journey

Abandoned Guilt and Absorbed Gladness

My 4,718-day IVF journey

Ericka Michelle Richburg

with C. NaTasha Richburg

Abandoned Guilt and Absorbed Gladness: My 4,718-day IVF journey
by Ericka Michelle Richburg with C. NaTasha Richburg

© Copyright 2021
SAINT PAUL PRESS, DALLAS, TEXAS

ISBN: 9798789638477

Printed in the U.S.A.

Contents

Dedicated to Erielle

Thank you…
To everyone who prayed for me,
stayed with me, and played with me
so I could enjoy life again, thank you!

Ericka's Introduction

My story will help many who struggle with infertility, contemplate weight loss surgery, and deal with divorce or toxic relationships, both romantic and platonic. This story is for individuals who diligently try not to give up hope and simply look for a glimmer of light at the end of a very dark tunnel. Maybe it's hard for you to see things getting better. A positive outcome seems like something that happens to other people. The crescendo of mountain top experience is coming. I am here to say, "Stand boldly in your truth," the smile will take shape one day soon. I stand firmly in my truth throughout the pages of this book. I am glad to smile again as I prepare to tell you about my journey characterized as a roller coaster ride. Spoiler alert, I made it. I'm better for it.

What I have been through is not for the faint at heart. I have given birth to a beautiful, intelligent, witty daughter. My loving and supportive parents have acted in a ride-or-die capacity to cheer me on and stand at the bottom of my fall with a safety net ready to catch me anytime I need encouragement. I am incredibly grateful for my birthday twin, who is my brother. We are four years apart and share the same birthday; he is funny and makes me smile. God is good. I am forever grateful for family!

I look forward to one day fully embracing a loving relationship with a man who cherishes and respects me beyond my wildest dreams. I choose to resist the guilt of being a single parent. I am ready to celebrate in gladness the hope of a brighter tomorrow.

Guilt: /gilt/
Noun, The fact of having committed a specified or implied offense or crime.

Verb (Informal), Make (someone) feel guilty, especially to induce them to do something.

Gladness /glad·nuhs/,
Noun,
A condition of supreme wellbeing and good spirits

C. NaTasha's (Mommy) Introduction

Ericka's two dismissed cases led me to believe that something very toxic was occurring in her home. My daughter was not her loving, bubbly self. Something was off-kilter. However, I didn't honestly know what was happening. I knew that my husband and I must continue to be "Team Ericka" regardless of her circumstances.

The good thing about letting my kids attend speaking engagements with me is that the sessions taught them life lessons. The life-changing imprints of my training sessions moved to the front of their brain when needed. One presentation I gave changed Ericka's life forever. The lesson was titled, "Let go of the rope." I needed the audience to understand that playing tug of war with toxic people has no value. Simply let go of the rope. Watch the poisonous person fall away and fall on their butt when you let go of the rope.

After one extremely toxic event in Ericka's home, she let go of the rope. She stopped trying to hold onto the rope of a relationship surrounded by a fan club of fake mean-spirited people posing as well-intended friends. Ericka let go of the rope to breathe life into this story filled with lessons to help others learn to let go of the rope and know it's okay to have a rough patch in life. This book is Ericka's story. This story aims to share the life-changing events Ericka experienced to get to the light at the end of the tunnel to the experience of the gladness of giving birth to a baby girl.

Chapter 1
Introduction

"Train up a child in the way he should go,
And when he is old he will not depart from it."

— Proverb 22:6

My name is Ericka Michelle, the daughter of C. NaTasha and Melvin Richburg. I am the eldest of four children and the first sibling to encounter "life experiences." As the firstborn, I had babysitting opportunities and experienced the advantage of being the first to leave home and attend college. I also held the erroneous belief that I would be the first to have a child. If there is a real "baby whisperer," it would be me. As an infant teacher at a childcare center, I trained babies to roll over, crawl, and roll their lips to make bubbles (raspberries). Some of the children in my care wanted me to be a loving member of their families. I love children, and children love me.

In December 2006, I married at the age of 20. I had bright hopes of building a family with my husband and little ones filling our home. To my dismay, it was not in the cards for me to have children effortlessly and spend the rest of my picture-perfect life with a doting husband, gazing into the cherubic faces of our happy children. While not what I expected, my path to motherhood is not a stereotypical story of love. This story describes the love of family, friends, co-workers, and members of my IVF Facebook group, whose collective stories afforded me the support I needed for this roller coaster ride. The funny thing about the roller coaster ride is, I don't have the stomach for it. The downward drop of the roller coaster has my jaws flopping in the wind. I am pushed back by the wind, so much so that I can't scream. In physical terror, I can't yell out the joyous screams with a robust zeal amid controlled trepidation. My screams at the amusement park were not heroic, though fortified with fear beyond imagination.

This story is about the roller coaster ride of my life that did not include a dotting husband, ideal weight, or picture-perfect health. My life's ride was without a loving spouse who wished the best for me. My reality meant that I moved everything from my marriage apartment, immediately took my name off the lease, and moved back to my childhood family home when COVID-19 stopped the world in its tracks. My mother became both my life coach and birthing coach. My brother supported me at my lowest points with cards and gifts, hoping to lift my spirits, and my dad prayed we made it through this trying time together with a sound mind and spirit. This new reality destined me to help others navigate similar paths I have taken. This story describes the series of events that took place on my path to motherhood.

Chapter 2
The Start of the
Roller Coaster Ride

"Life is a journey, not a destination."

— Ralph Waldo Emerson

Resting in the dreams of a newlywed with fresh memories of the vast glow of "I do," the prospect of the predestined first child to be conceived on our honeymoon night was an absolute outcome of marriage, so I thought. At the beginning of our marriage, we assumed it was always true that couples conceive on their wedding night. Since we had the glowing shimmer of honeymoon blitz as the wing beneath our wings, there was no reason to believe differently, or was there? Once back home to begin life in the routine of day-to-day living, I took a pregnancy test. We waited impatiently to read the positive sign on the pee stick. Impatiently patient about the forthcoming celebration, I prepared to smile and embrace the new life growing in me. NOPE! The fairy tale of wedding night conception did not proceed as I initially believed. It ultimately took 4,718 days, equivalent to 12 years, 11 months, 7 hours, and 25 minutes for my dream of becoming a mother to come true.

I eventually gave birth to my first child after being strapped into the emotional roller coaster ride. The ride required me to hold tight to the safety bar resting on my lap to survive the drop from the top of the roller coaster, just after the first drop, where the swing around the curve as it jerks my head back, cramping the neck while bracing for the climb to the next perk in the ride. In the years leading up to conceiving my daughter, I had many surgeries and medical procedures. Every time I went in for surgery, I never felt nervous. There was no tightness in my neck-like while swinging around the curve on the roller coaster. I hoped the slow ride up before the coaster's first drop offered great anticipation for great things to come. Keep in mind, I trusted God to guide the hands of my extraordinarily qualified surgeons. I always felt confident that going under anesthesia would allow for painless surgery and rectify my infertility problem. I kept my focus only on those individuals who stayed with me for this ride. Those who fell off along the way are not mentioned here in my account.

Ericka's Fertility Journey

Chapter 3
Polycystic Ovary Syndrome (PCOS)

"You must be the change you wish to see in the world."

— Gandhi

Newlyweds living in Columbus, Ohio, I did not get pregnant on our honeymoon night. So, I sought the help of a fertility specialist to check my female inner workings to prepare me for conception. Excited to make sure everything was okay with me, I never thought anything was wrong. I just wanted to have a doctor validate everything was working correctly. The doctor learned from the blood work and from other tests that I had some issues that may impact fertility. I found out I had polycystic ovary syndrome (PCOS)[1] as an issue inhibiting my quest to conceive. PCOS also affected my ability to lose and

---

[1] Polycystic ovary syndrome (**PCOS**) is a hormonal disorder common among women of reproductive age. Women with **PCOS** may have infrequent or prolonged menstrual periods or excess male hormone (androgen) levels. The ovaries may develop numerous small collections of fluid (follicles) and fail to regularly release eggs. Source: https://www.google.com/search?q=pcos&rlz=1C5CHFA_enUS773US776&oq=PCOS&aqs=chrome.0.0l8.2061j0j8&sourceid=chrome&ie=UTF-8

maintain weight. Anytime I ate more than 500 calories, I gained weight. I continued to gain weight. The doctor wasn't concerned about the weight gain at that time, so I wasn't either. My husband and I approached the issue by implementing timed intercourse and taking a medication called Clomiphene or Clomid, a pill taken orally for five days to treat infertility in women who do not ovulate. Six months of this method resulted in nothing. No pregnancy. No baby. Yet, no reason not to give up hope.

I took the next step on the roller coaster ride toward pregnancy, which included an elective laparoscopy, "[a] surgical procedure in which a fiber-optic instrument is inserted through the abdominal wall to view the organs in the abdomen or to permit a surgical procedure" (Lexico.com/em/definition/laparoscopy). In other words, the doctor sent a tiny camera into my body through my belly button to see what was happening inside of me. Yet again, the doctor did not find any concerning issues. However, I was confused because if they could not find any issues to be concerned about why couldn't I get pregnant? Since the doctors weren't worried, I carried my private concern alone. The sense of shame associated with an inability to get pregnant began to become a weight strapped to my neck that made it difficult to lift my head when well-intending people asked, "When are you planning to have children?" The answer rested deep inside my heart, trusting God would grant my wish to carry a child. Unfortunately, this was the up climb of a multiple drop roller coaster. PCOS climb dropped me down into the surgical procedure called Intrauterine Insemination (IUI).

Chapter 4

Intrauterine Insemination (IUI)

"Never confuse a single defeat with a final defeat."

— F. Scott Fitzgerald

In 2010, my husband joined the military, and we were stationed in North Carolina. This opportunity provided me access to a military installation that performed fertility procedures at the clinic; better still, all the required medication was free of charge. The joyful splendor to be able to remain on the roller coaster's upswing, affording me access to fertility specialists, was an electrical charge I needed to believe I was nearing the end of the ride. Just like my first fertility specialists, the military clinic took blood work and performed testing. One test administered is called hysterosalpingography (HSG),[2] which required an x-ray of the Fallopian tubes. The necessary

---

[2] An **HSG** is a special kind of x-ray used to evaluate female fertility. An outpatient procedure, the test takes no longer than a half hour. It involves placing an iodine-based dye through the cervix and taking x-rays. These x-rays help evaluate the shape of the uterus and whether the fallopian tubes are blocked. Source: https://www.verywellfamily.com/does-an-hsg-hurt-1960165

yet very uncomfortable examination revealed my left Fallopian tube was blocked due to scarring. I had endometriosis.[3] The endometriosis combined with PCOS caused many complications. First, PCOS caused me to gain a large amount of weight that eventually qualified me for weight loss surgery that would not take place until 2013. Second, the endometriosis required that I proceed with Intrauterine Insemination (IUI).[4]

An IUI cycle consists of injecting hormonal medications Gonal-F and Menopur into the stomach while the doctor monitors my progress every other day with a sonogram and blood work. Once all hormonal and blood levels look good, the nurse calls and instructs me to inject a *very long needle* (known as a trigger shot) into my buttocks to ensure ovulation. The ovulation timing is critical. Please note that this step requires teamwork because I could not inject the needle into the buttocks myself. The administration of the trigger shot required that all involved adopted the precision of a world-class rowing team. The trigger shot contained a medication called Human Chronic Gonadotrophin (HCG). The medicine is essential since it allows the stimulated ovary to release

---

[3] **Endometriosis** (en-doe-me-tree-O-sis) is an often painful disorder in which tissue similar to the tissue that normally lines the inside of your uterus — the endometrium — grows outside your uterus. **Endometriosis** most commonly involves your ovaries, fallopian tubes, and the tissue lining your pelvis. **Symptoms:** Dysmenorrhea; Pelvic pain Source: https://www.mayoclinic.org/diseases-conditions/endometriosis/symptoms-causes/syc-20354656

[4] Intrauterine Insemination (**IUI**) is a fertility treatment that involves placing sperm inside a woman's uterus to facilitate fertilization. The goal of **IUI** is to increase the number of sperm that reach the fallopian tubes and subsequently increase the chance of fertilization. Source: https://americanpregnancy.org/getting-pregnant/intrauterine-insemination/

eggs in preparation for insemination 24-36 hours later in the doctor's office.

On the day of the insemination, we would go to an external facility where my husband would collect his sperm sample. The staff would wash the sperm sample using a particular solution to preserve it. This procedure cost $160 each time we did it. Then I would transport the collection cup between my breasts to keep the sperm warm. When I arrived at the hospital on the military post, I would give the nurse the sample, she would place it in a catheter, and then place the catheter into my uterus. I lay still for a few minutes before being sent home to rest. I returned to the hospital two weeks later to get my blood drawn to see if the procedure was successful. We underwent IUI 4 times, and each time the treatment was unsuccessful. During this very trying time, it was difficult to see the light at the end of the tunnel. The next step was in-Vitro Fertilization (IVF). I was prepared to remain on the roller coaster ride.

Chapter 5
In-Vitro Fertilization (IVF)

"Do what you have to do until
you don't have to do it anymore."

— C. NaTasha Richburg

In August 2011, we decided to proceed with in-vitro fertilization (IVF).[5] One great memory of the preparation for IVF included the familiar drama of the trigger shot.[6] The notion that I had to participate in the process of poking my body with a needle was daunting. To say I am petrified of needles is an understatement. When we were young, my father worked nights and was responsible for taking us for doctor checkups arranged by my mother. My siblings laughed at me because I would scream with the zeal of a siren at its highest pitch before the doctor came close with the vaccination needle. I still hate

---

[5] **In vitro fertilization** is an assisted reproductive technology (ART) commonly referred to as **IVF**. **IVF** is the **process** of **fertilization** by extracting eggs, retrieving a sperm sample, and then manually combining an egg and sperm in a laboratory dish. The embryo(s) is then transferred to the uterus. Source: https://americanpregnancy.org/infertility/in-vitro-fertilization/

[6] Trigger shot is an important part of the IVF timeline. The purpose of the IVF trigger shot is **to send eggs into a state of reproductive division called meiosis, also known as maturation division**, during the 36-hour period preceding ovulation or retrieval. Jan 7, 2021 Source: https://coastalfertility.com/trigger-shot-for-ivf-and-its-importance/

needles, though I have a clearer understanding of their importance. So, let's be clear: preparing for the injection is like standing next to a team with Double-Dutch ropes during an active Double-Dutch competition. According to The National Double Dutch League, "Double Dutch is a rope skipping exercise played when two ropes are turned in eggbeater fashion." While the ropes are turning, I sway front and back, trying to sync with the ropes' rhythm. The process of swaying is what I do to generate the nerve to jump to take the trigger shot. In other words, getting up the nerve to inject the trigger shot into me is a momentous occasion. If you don't mind needles, it's not that bad. But if you hate needles like me, the process of taking the trigger shot requires heroic courage.

It took six months for us to save enough money to pay for the IVF procedure. The cost was $6,997. I worked to save half; we took out a loan for the other half. An added blessing was that the medication is given free of charge as part of our healthcare plan. In February 2012, we proceeded with IVF, like IUI, except I had my eggs retrieved under local anesthesia. My husband provided his sample in the cup, as in the IUI process, and the doctor washed the sperm. Next, the embryologist combined the egg and sperm in a petri dish. At the time of retrieval, the doctor collected 15 eggs. Five days later, the best embryo was selected and placed into my uterus. Two weeks after this grand production, I returned to have my blood drawn to determine if I was pregnant; I was not. All of my hard work, time, dedication, and financial sacrifice were all for nothing. I was heartbroken with a downtrodden spirit that covered my face with a veil of shame. To exhale with the understanding that I was not pregnant, I took a sabbatical from work. I was so embarrassed to admit to friends and co-workers that I had not achieved my dream of motherhood. From 2012 until 2014, I traveled as part of the military duties with my husband to focus on other things besides trying to conceive.

In May 2013, my husband received orders to move to Fort Campbell. While living there, I revisited the desire to have children. My Polycystic Ovary Syndrome (PCOS) was in full effect. During this time, I had reached my heaviest weight of 237.1 pounds on my small 5'1" frame. That was an abundance of heaviness filled with sorrows for me to carry. I was eating correctly and exercising on occasion, but the weight would not budge. I went to see my primary care physician about infertility problems. My doctor asked me if I had ever thought about weight loss surgery. I said I hadn't, but I wanted to learn more about it. Out of the many options given, I chose the gastric sleeve to remove a portion of my stomach. A small stomach will limit my ability to consume too much food. In July 2014, I had weight loss surgery as a step that could possibly help me conceive. I was not overwhelmed by the weight loss surgery.

Instead, I was cool as a cucumber. The surgery was necessary to ensure I meet my weight loss goal of at least one hundred pounds reduction in weight.

The day came for the surgery that would help me one day be at an ideal weight to conceive. Just before going under anesthesia, the Chaplain asked if I wanted prayer. I told him "no" because I can pray for myself. When the time arrived to get prepped for surgery, the nurses had difficulty getting an IV (intravenous) needle into my vein. The nurses called in a particular anesthesiologist. The specialist was successful at what the others failed to do. After he completed his job, he asked if he could pray for me. I allowed him to because we built a rapport in a short amount of time. Because of the beautiful genuine connection established by the specialist, once I recovered, I decided to attend his church called the LifePoint Church. That specialist is a testimony that divine intervention can also benefit outside of the surgical setting. It shows the importance of how being nice to people can be a witness of God's grace and goodness. From that point forward, LifePoint Church located in Clarksville, Tennessee, has been my gauge of a great church experience.

In January 2016, after exactly 18 months, I reached the milestone of 100 pounds lost! In 2016, my husband and I decided to divorce without winning the victory against infertility. My inability to conceive had weighed heavily on our marriage. I wanted my husband to go on and have a family, something I couldn't give him. The roller coaster ride felt like another fast drop of hopes for conception. Ready to get off the ride because of the challenging ups and downs, I decided to rest and just stop trying to get pregnant. Willing to take the next upswing of the roller coaster with a lower expectation of a successful conclusion, was worth the ride. I never imagined the journey to conception and childbirth would take more medical procedures and a chance meeting with a brilliant doctor from Johns Hopkins University who discovered the cause of my infertility. So, I held on tightly, preparing to reach the top of the roller coaster to plunge into in-Vitro Fertilization (IVF) revisited.

Chapter 6
In-Vitro Fertilization (IVF) Revisited

"Embrace obstacles to build the resilience required to live a purpose-driven life."

— Viktor Frankl

In 2017, I was married for a second time. My husband suggested I see a specialist about my infertility. In May of that year, I went to a fertility specialist in Maryland at Johns Hopkins University hospital. The doctor conducted an exploratory procedure to see what was going on reproductively. The specialist found that my Fallopian tubes were leaking, which represented a condition called hydrosalpinx.[7] The doctor believed the leaking might have caused my infertility in 2012. The specialist removed my Fallopian tubes and informed me that the only way I could

---

[7] Hydrosalpinx can be caused by an old infection in the fallopian tubes. Other causes include previous surgery (particularly surgeries on the tube), severe adhesions of your pelvis, endometriosis, or other sources of infection such as appendicitis Source: https://www.reproductivefacts.org/news-and-publications/patient-fact-sheets-and-booklets/documents/fact-sheets-and-info-booklets/hydrosalpinx/

conceive was through IVF. I was distraught at the news; I felt less of a woman. Having a baby was the only thing I'd ever wanted to do in life and that was taken away from me. I knew that the cost of IVF was astronomical. Leaving the hospital with the devastating yet hopeful news, was like a quick whip around the curve onto the up-ramp of the roller coaster, taking on the last major up climb before the final plunge at the end of the ride.

My employer offered health insurance with comprehensive infertility coverage, but the cost of the procedure and the medication was still too high. For personal reasons, I switched jobs, and with my new position came reasonably priced health insurance and comprehensive infertility coverage. With my new insurance coverage in hand, I made a doctor's appointment.

- In January 2019, I made an appointment at a fertility center in Columbia, Maryland. During my first consultation with my doctor, I received a checklist of everything I needed to complete to be ready for IVF.
- In February 2019, I had a saline sonogram, which helps determine if any abnormalities are present within the uterus.
- In April 2019, the test revealed three polyps. The removal of polyps threw a wrench into my plans.

- In May 2019, my employer switched insurance carriers in the middle of the term, and my doctor's office did not accept what would have been my new insurance.

- In June 2019, I switched employers. I now work for a wonderful healthcare organization that offers fertility and prescription coverage.

- In July 2019, my new insurance took effect. So, I was back on track, completing my checklist.

- In August 2019, I began taking birth control to regulate my cycle and quiet things down, and then I underwent a baseline ultrasound.

- On September 20, 2019, I had 35 eggs retrieved. Due to my PCOS, I suffered from Ovarian Hyperstimulation Syndrome (OHSS).[8] My body was so bloated and swollen that I could not have an immediate, fresh transfer. My treatment team had me drink *Gatorade Zero* until my hormones balanced out. While I waited, I asked about clinical trials. I participated in a clinical trial that involved a research study evaluating whether the individualized timing of embryo transfer is superior to the standard timing of embryo transfer, called Endometrial Receptivity Analysis (ERA).[9] The biopsy

---

[8]Ovarian hyperstimulation syndrome is an exaggerated response to excess hormones. It usually occurs in women taking injectable hormone medications to stimulate the development of eggs in the ovaries. Ovarian hyperstimulation syndrome (OHSS) causes the ovaries to swell and become painful. Source: https://www.mayoclinic.org/diseases-conditions/ovarian-hyperstimulation-syndrome-ohss/symptoms-causes/syc-20354697

[9]Endometrial Receptivity Analysis (ERA), is a genetic test that takes a small sample of a woman's endometrial lining to determine which day would be the best day to transfer the embryo during an IVF cycle. Source: https://www.igenomix.com/fertility-challenges/what-to-know-about-endometrial-receptivity-analysis/

brought me the opportunity to have my embryos undergo Preimplantation Genetic Screening (PGS).[10] The results indicated that, of the 35 eggs retrieved, only 4 made it to blastocyst, and of those 4, only two were normal.

- On October 21, 2019, I had an ERA biopsy.

- On November 22, 2019, I completed my frozen embryo transfer. I went into the transfer with a full bladder, as instructed, and the doctor inserted the catheter. I watched the monitor as my embryo entered my uterus. After the procedure was completed, I went home and relaxed, but I made a point to continue with my routine and not to let worry or fear consume me. I began taking pregnancy tests two days after the transfer (far too soon), but I did not receive a positive result until seven days later.

- On November 29, 2019, I received my very first positive pregnancy test after 12 years and 11 months of trying to conceive.

- On December 6, 2019, I went into the office to take a blood test to determine whether I was officially pregnant. My beta level was 1654, and I went back

---

[10]**Preimplantation genetic testing** (PGT) includes the examination of embryos during in vitro fertilization (IVF) before the possible transfer to a woman's uterus for a range of **genetic** problems that can cause implantation failure, miscarriage, and birth defects in a resulting child. Source: https://fertility.womenandinfants.org/treatment/genetic-testing

three days later to make sure the levels were rising correctly – the second beta was 6709.

- On December 19, 2019, I was six weeks, five days pregnant with my daughter, whom I saw on the sonogram for the very first time and heard her heartbeat. From that point on, I affectionately called her Itty Bitty.
- On December 29, 2006, I embarked on the journey of becoming a mother. My dreams had come true.
- On March 16, 2020, my life changed again. I never dreamed that I'd be expecting my first daughter during a worldwide pandemic, though I am thankful for the journey and my current health.
- August 2020 was the expected due date for my daughter to come into the world.

I looked forward to being her mother. I want to explore life through her eyes and help her discover her dreams and fulfill her passions. I also learned in my home that I was the only one excited about my pregnancy. The process up to conception was not that of a loving couple holding hands, waiting for the heartbeat. I alone was excited about the prospect of my pregnancy. The very slow churn to the top of

the roller coast loomed with the quarantine measures of
COVID -19.[11]

---

[11]According to the <u>Centers for Disease Control</u>, "*On February 11, 2020, the World Health Organization announced an official name for the disease: coronavirus disease 2019, abbreviated COVID-19. 'CO' stands for 'corona,' 'VI' for 'virus,' and 'D' for disease. The virus that causes COVID-19, SARS-CoV-2, is a coronavirus. The word corona means crown and refers to the appearance that coronaviruses get from the spike proteins sticking out of them. COVID-19 is a dangerous disease caused by a virus discovered in December 2019 in Wuhan, China. It is very contagious and has quickly spread around the world.*"

Pandemic, Pregnancy, and Proceeding with Purpose

Chapter 7
Beautiful Mistake

"Do the best you can until you know better.
Then when you know better, do better."

— Maya Angelou

Trying to work on my marriage was difficult when I was the only person putting in the effort to make it work. I was alone in that endeavor. I simply paid half of the rent, was the caretaker of his children, the purchaser of kid's beds, clothes, and anything else that would make them happy in the apartment. During the marriage, 2nd (not to be referred to as my husband from this point forward) had a Facebook status that never read "married." Not taking that as a sign to "get out" of the marriage, I failed to take to heart the warning from his co-workers who said, "watch him because 2nd does not tell anyone he is married to you." He would not wear his wedding ring and accused me, rightly so, of telling my mother everything. I would not allow 2nd's behavior towards me to remain a secret. My mother knew everything. However, my mother never treated 2nd like a mother scorned by the negative behavior imposed on her daughter. She acted as my confidant who also told me when I was wrong; 2nd did not recognize that truth.

I lived a living hell with 2nd's family members thinking it was okay to verbally chastise me in person, on the phone, on social media, and behind my back. Some of them are well-meaning yet meaning me well was not a choice they executed in writing. The negative crew participated in disparaging posts about me on social media. I was taught not to respond to negativity, so I never replied to their comments publicly.

Still, in the glow of my first pregnancy, 2nd gave me the news that he did not want to remain married to me. I obliged his wish. I was ill-informed about who he was as a person when we first met. His behavioral secrets remain oblivious to me. I did not understand that I would remain a secret. I was a secret wife so much so that when we divorced, he didn't have to make an announcement that I moved out. Yet, the worst of times with him turned into the best of times for me after my dream of becoming pregnant came true.

IFV process happened with the sperm donated to me by 2nd. For this book, a sperm donor is an individual who gives a sperm sample to support the development of an embryo. The donor paid nothing for the expensive IFV process, never inquired about the conception process or followed up during the pregnancy regarding the status of the pregnancy. I was alone throughout the 40-week maternity process. No midnight runs to get food for cravings, no leg rubs and stomach touches, only rude comments deemed to upset the pregnant woman. I tried not to let him upset me.

Being married to 2nd was a beautiful mistake because he suggested I get my fertility issue checked. Having gone through many different procedures over a ten-year period, I thought I didn't need another thing checked out. To appease 2nd, I checked out my fertility status with a new doctor at Johns Hopkins University. The doctor discovered I had leaking tubes. The tubes were removed, and I got pregnant as described in the fertility section of this book. Marrying 2nd was my beautiful mistake. This is the last mention of 2nd; he will not be spoken of again.

Chapter 8
Pregnant with Purpose

"Storms don't come to teach us painful lessons;
rather, they were meant to wash us clean."

— Shannon L. Alder

There are times when I prayed for a positive pregnancy test only to naively believe the occasion would be happy. Being able to say out loud for the first time in 33 years of life on this planet, "I am pregnant!" felt like a beautiful twilight of my dreams. Texting friends and family with the news was a rite of passage to all who knew my journey. Those who were not happy about my pregnancy news are not included in the vocabulary of my future dreams. I choose to ride the roller coaster of my life up the incline to reach the place of gladness and happy new beginnings. I will never stop the feeling of excitement for the precious time filled with my pregnancy glow. Only people who love and care for me are welcomed into my precious space filled with the growing light of my unborn daughter.

The grueling state of the pandemic caused a mental health crisis in America. I felt a bit of loneliness associated with the stay-at-home orders given as part of American's shutdown. The following is a partial list from the timeline of COVID-19 developments in 2020.

A Timeline of COVID-19 Developments in 2020

January 1, 2021

AJMC Staff

https://www.ajmc.com/view/a-timeline-of-covid19-developments-in-2020

- *February 3 — the US Declares Public Health Emergency*
- *March 11 — WHO Declares COVID-19 a Pandemic*
- *March 13 — Travel Ban on Non-US Citizens Traveling From Europe Goes Into Effect*
- *March 19 — California Issues Statewide Stay-at-Home Order*
- *March 26 — Senate Passes CARES Act*
- *May 28 — US COVID-19 Deaths Pass the 100,000 Mark*
- *June 10 — US COVID-19 Cases Reach 2 Million*

- *June 16 — HHS Announces COVID-19 Vaccine Doses Will Be Free for Some*

COVID Data Tracker

https://covid.cdc.gov/covid-data-tracker/#datatracker-home

As of July 18, 2021, Cases: 33,877,470 ~~ Deaths: 606,526

My hardships feel lighter because of the hilarious recounting of occurrences throughout my pregnancy. We want to tell the story about the difficulty of being a black woman while pregnant. This story will show how some well-meaning people did not represent me well during the birthing process. The roller coaster ride drops into the trials associated with the pandemic and worldwide social isolation. We can make it through with God's grace and mercy.

Chapter 9
The Baby Shower
(A Mother's Perspective)

"And as we let our own light shine,
we unconsciously give other people
permission to do the same."

— Marianne Williamson

As Ericka's mother, I wanted to give a first-person perspective of Ericka's story. Presented here is my recollection of what happened just before and after the birth of Ericka's daughter. Life forced us to fill our pandemic baskets with "noes," "you can't leave home unless going to work," "standing in food lines 6 feet apart," and "full of worry that the new normal may keep us caged in the house indefinitely."

During better times, our favorite thing to do as a mother/daughter team is to shop. Oh yeah, we can window shop with the best of them. We don't need money to go out to look and hope for a sale. Finding a reasonably priced item is a mission. Designer labels are not our passion. As mother and daughter, we love to visit "Home Goods." Shopping at Home Goods is our number one bonding experience. When Home Goods closed with the rest of the world during the pandemic, we cruised the aisles in our minds within our fond pre-pandemic memories of happy times, within the store's boundary. We laugh and giggle at the fun we had together in the store. To facilitate new memories of Home Goods during the pandemic, we'd drive by, stop and look at the front door of the store, longing for the day that the doors would open again. We would look at the store's front door, hoping to be invited in for a secret peek at new merchandise. Of course, the miraculous special opening never happened.

The underwhelming feeling of being stuck indoors consisted of gazing out of the patio doors of our home watching the birds jockeying for position on our deck. The birds would fight for territory, bathe in the rain, and demonstrate for us the beautiful daily movement of wildlife. The pandemic relegated local wildlife "as new owners of the outside." The deer, groundhogs, and foxes brazenly hand danced across the lawn in sync with the tune "If This World Were Mine." Surviving the pandemic required dreaming for a new life beyond our residence. We wanted to move freely amongst people in festival crowds again. This season of gratefulness allowed us to thank God for a loving environment in which to live. We had our daughter, Ericka residing with us, safe and sound. We are forever grateful that God's hand touched Ericka's reproductive system to prepare her womb for pregnancy and subsequent motherhood. We planned an exciting baby shower within the governing Centers of Diseases Control (CDC) guidance's scope. We used Zoom to adhere to every requirement of the CDC guidance.

How to Protect Yourself & Others Updated June 11, 2021
https://www.cdc.gov/coronavirus/2019-ncov/prevent-getting-sick/prevention.html

- Wear a mask
- Stay 6 feet away from others
- Get Vaccinated
- Avoid crowds and poorly ventilated spaces
- Wash your hands often
- Cover coughs and sneezes
- Clean and disinfect
- Monitor your health daily

The CDC COVID-19 restrictions felt like wearing very tight jeans on an intercontinental flight, making it a very uncomfortable ride. If I don't undo my belt and relieve pressure on my waste, blotting will occur. So, when I go on long flights, I wear loose-fitting clothing. COVID-19 did not prepare me to pick proper attire, and I struggled to prepare for the new and life-changing journey.

Our family's "new normal" made it imperative to be the best support system for Ericka's pregnancy. She carried the title "single parent" as a weight, though we believe her to be simply an "awesome parent" as the attribute to characterize her quest for motherhood. "I don't want a baby shower," Ericka said with the cloud of loneliness covering her eyes. "Well, don't because I will have a shower. And yes, you are invited. I will invite all of my friends. Please give me the names of your friends and people you work with, so I can invite them to my shower," I said with smiles and energy forged by the notion the best is yet to come. "I will be darned if I let the circumstance imposed on my child make this a less than joyous occasion," I thought. So, I began to work through the mechanics of our Zoom baby shower. I am incredibly familiar with Zoom as a technology used for business and sorority meetings. For sorority use, I learned that some people struggle with using Zoom.

The baby shower invitation was sent via text. Only those who RSVPed were presented a gift box to bring to the screen during the baby shower. The online shopping for the shower gift boxes was fun. "Let's make your shower the best. We need to purchase gift boxes filled with fun stuff," I said.

Ericka began to wriggle a smile's worth of energy on her face. She was starting to feed into the notion that having a baby shower is a way family and friends can show love. She needed a lot of love to carry her through the pregnancy.

I have a Google deficit, meaning, I don't Google well. Ericka helped me. She can Google as well as a world-class Google champion who has the trophies to prove it. She can find anything using a Google search. Ericka helped me plan and prepare for the baby shower. "Yes, let's get this done. I know people like chocolate. Let's get chocolate, games, favors, and thank you notes. Let's have games. I want people to answer questions and give prizes to everyone who comes. Let's go shopping online for shower gifts," I said to Ericka at the top of my lungs with great excitement with the hope that she will feel the love that friends and family will give her new life. The sadness associated with being a single parent lifted when the prospect of shopping came into view.

Many of the guests used the online ordering process to have their gifts delivered directly to our home. Ericka and I wrapped all baby shower gifts delivered directly to our house. That chore was fun for both Ericka and me.

On the morning of the Zoom baby shower, I entirely decorated the room as if the guests would arrive at our house in person. Gifts stacked against the wall were in full display in various colors for the Zoom camera to capture the moment.

Balloons draped the windows, along with a sign that said "baby girl." The baby shower tablecloth was in place to accentuate the joyous occasion. My daughter-in-love came on time to our home to help us with the games and gift presentations for the online audience. We were grateful that my daughter-in-love worked lovingly to lift our spirits with the hustling attitude of a servant leader.

On the screen were at least 12 beautiful shower attendees. Love came out of the screen into our room. Wearing a beautiful off-shoulder striped dress that flowed perfectly over her growing stomach, Ericka captivated the beauty of the celebration. Her hair was braided and adorned with a beautiful crown. Operation baby shower was on. We played games, starting with "How many chocolate candies are in my jar."

"60....40 .... Close... 38.... 36....no....up... 47...less... 42... yes!! Right –Ms. C, you win."

"How many days did it take for Ericka to get pregnant. 1,000 ~ up ~ 2,000 – up ~~ 8,000 ~ heck no!!! – "you just don't want me to win," said Cousin Dee. "That's not true," I said. "Cousin Dee! Cousin Dee! Where did she go! Your screen is dark. Where are you?" Collectively the gang said, "Dee, turn on your camera." "Okay," Dee replied. Once the camera came on, we heard, "Hey everybody, I am back." Everyone laughed. We continued with the guessing game of "How many days did it take for Ericka to get pregnant." The fun continued, "—4,000-- "Close enough. Lil, you win." "Yayyyy!" the group collectively yells.

With joy and laughter in her voice, Cousin Dee chants, "How come I never win…. I want to win." "Okay, everybody will win today," I said.

Tee Tee signed into the Zoom, turned off her camera, and continued her life without participating. Unbeknownst to her, her phone was not on mute. Everyone could hear her conversation. Collectively, the group shouted at the screen. "Tee Tee, You're not on mute. You're not on mute! We can hear you have a conversation with your mechanic." Tee Tee continued her conversation with the mechanic and never came back to join the festivities. We continued our fun and games without Tee Tee. It was a good day.

The day was so much fun. The time limit of the free Zoom did not allow for the opening of the baby shower gifts on camera. We videoed Ericka's gift opening and sent the video to all of the participates. The operation, "We are no longer going to be sad," the shower was a success. Ericka felt the love from others, and the dream of becoming a mom was in full effect. The time was approaching for Ericka to go to the hospital to have her baby girl.

Chapter 10
The Baby Is On the Way

*"I prayed for this child, and the Lord has granted me
what I asked of him. So now I give him to the Lord.
For his whole life he will be given over to the Lord."*

— I Samuel 1:27 & 28

(Hannah Dedicates Samuel)

**On November 22, 2019, the embryo transfer took place.
On Sunday, November 22, 2020, Ericka's baby girl was
dedicated to God.**

The time had finally arrived. The doctor's office returned
Ericka's call about excessive swelling. She needed to have
her blood pressure taken immediately. As a mother, I knew her
blood pressure was high. I privately feared danger was
lingering. With five pieces of pink lounge, baby gear, car seat,
blanket, and snacks, Ericka and I hurried to the doctor's office
to confirm my biggest fear. Ericka was ready to pop. We

gathered our stuff, rushed through the kitchen to reach the door to the garage, winged the door open, and bam! No car. The car is gone. Where is the vehicle! Where - is – the – doggone – CAR? Oh, no, I completely forgot: Melvin, Ericka's father, took my car for an oil change. Both Ericka and I thought in a mind-to-mind conclusion, "We can't go anywhere in daddy's dirty car."

The car is filthy inside and outside. I love my man. I appreciate his unique way to rock his desires outside of the norm. However, a dirty vehicle is too far outside of the standard of cleanliness for us. "Our only option is to drive the Fiat," I said. The Fiat comfortably seats two people. It was challenging to fit five pieces of pink lounge, baby gear, car seat, blanket, and snacks inside the tiny car. "I will call Daddy to have him bring my car to the doctor's office," I said to Ericka, trying to appear calm. I said, "We will trade cars with Daddy while you go inside the doctor's office to have your blood pressure taken."

By God's grace, we squeezed ourselves into the tiny Fiat. Two ladies, one pregnant and ready to pop, five pieces of pink bags, blanket and snacks, and baby stuff, safely got to the doctor's office. Focused and in mommy mode, I was ready to go into the doctor's office and speak to someone and find out if my daughter could now be released to go to the hospital's labor and delivery department? The doctor agreed to send Ericka to the hospital directly from his office. Ericka learned from the doctor that she had pre-eclampsia.[12]

The ten-minute ride in my immaculate car to the hospital was joyous because we both appreciated riding in a comfortable, clean vehicle. Our laughter took the attention away from the fact that Ericka's swollen body was not healthy for the baby. We laughed, knowing Daddy would do everything possible to get to the doctor's office not to delay our trip to the hospital, and he did. Let the ride begin!

Early in the pregnancy, I purchased a substantially large blue maternity dress that would be comfortable for Ericka to wear in the ninth month of pregnancy. That blue dress was perfect for the occasion. I dropped Ericka off at labor and delivery, the same place I dropped her off at two months earlier, as a precautionary measure because of her high blood pressure and medium to high protein levels. Finally, 40 weeks into the pregnancy, we knew the lay of the land of the hospital even though COVID-19 protocol suspended tours and prenatal classes.

After I parked the car, I came into the hospital alone to meet Ericka. I met Ericka in the waiting room, which was uncharacteristically quiet because we were the only people present in the quiet space of COVID-19 restrictions. COVID-19 made for a calm hospital where guests were limited. No

---

[12]Preeclampsia and eclampsia are pregnancy-related high blood pressure disorders. Preeclampsia is a sudden spike in blood pressure. Eclampsia is more severe and can include **seizures** or coma. Source: https://www.nichd.nih.gov/health/topics/preeclampsia

crowded areas with family and friends anticipating a new birth. The hospital was quiet and very still. I wondered, where should I put five pieces of pink lounge, baby gear, car seat, blanket, and snacks?"

Chapter 11
Finally in the Hospital

*"God never allows pain without a purpose
in the lives of His children."*

— Jerry Bridges

Ericka got hooked up to the machinery that would monitor her labor and delivery. Her doctor was on vacation. The backup doctor was not answering the calls made by the hospital staff regarding the next steps since Ericka had dangerously high blood pressure. Her contractions read long and hard on the monitor though Ericka felt nothing.

Nothing was happening as far as giving my Ericka assistance by the nurses except when the machine alarm sounded when the baby was in distress. Eventually, a team of doctors thought it necessary to check on Ericka's dilation. The team of interns stood before Ericka. "I am going to see how much you have dilated," said the young doctor. "No, sir, your hands are too big," Ericka replied. Looking at both of his hands, the doctor said in a sad, almost promising voice, "My hands are not big. I think they are average." "No, sir," Ericka insisted, "your hands are too large. I want her to do it," she said, pointing at a more petite female doctor. "I want her," said Ericka. The male doctor eventually checked Ericka. "You have not dilated. If you don't have progress soon, we have to induce labor," said the doctor. "Where is my doctor's replacement?" said Ericka. "They have not responded to our calls," said the very attentive nurse. She made the entire ordeal seem manageable. That shift we named Candy Land. The room was well lit. The hospital staff, except the night nurse, were responsive to Ericka's needs.

When the shift changed, the night shift nurse was not very helpful. She was non-responsive to Ericka's inquiries which added to the perception of loneliness brought on by her lack of attention from her doctor. Ericka's doctor and backup were missing; the night-shift nurse was memorable but for the wrong reason. Ericka had an emergency C-Section. The baby was immediately transported to the Neonatal Intensive Care Unit (NICU) because she was having difficulty breathing.

Next, Ericka was moved to the mother/infant unit. We describe this unit as less than paradise. To add insult to injury, the nurse who entered Ericka's less than paradise room spoke in the meanest voice possible. The room was dark. The space was gloomy for us because the baby was transported directly to the Neonatal intensive care unit (NICU), getting extra oxygen. "HAVE YOU EVER HAD A BABY BEFORE?" was the greeting from the mean nurse. "No," said Ericka. Our focus at the time was the well-being of Ericka's baby girl, the baby girl that Ericka did not get an opportunity to lay her eyes on after the C-Section birth. I was able to take a picture of the baby and show Ericka her beautiful baby girl.

The mean nurse standing in front of us must have been a recent graduate of Grumpy University, a place where you failed if you smiled. I wanted to know as she lingered in the dark shadow of the dimly lit room, "HAVE YOU EVER HAD A BABY BEFORE?" I wanted to say, "You showed no empathy for what Ericka had just experienced giving birth to her daughter." I thought to myself, "Do patients speak well of your dark, gloomy Herman Munster persona?" I tried to figure out where I would put my five pieces of pink lounge, baby gear, car seat, blanket, and snacks in the tiny room. I wanted to know when I was going to NICU to see Ericka's baby? I wondered how I could sleep on the too-small chair for my 5' 1" frame? The grim reaper nurse fit in my count of the 99 problems.

When the baby was released from NICU to meet Ericka face-to-face for the first time, the following sunshiny day. The beautiful greeting of mother and newborn melted all of our worries away. We were grateful for the newness of the day. All was well, and the next day, the grim reaper nurse had a much better attitude. The hospital's COVID-19 policy granted one outside visitor other than myself. The darkroom with our grim reaper for a nurse felt brighter and more welcoming for my five pieces of pink lounge, baby gear, car seat, blanket, and snacks when the baby's Granddad came in bearing gifts and a smile. Just what we needed, sunshine to take away that room's dark shadow. We were going home in a few days.

With the pandemic in shutdown mode, we needed a way to celebrate with family and friends. From the hospital room, we sent out invitations for our Zoom Sip and See. We invited many people to attend our online event to shine a light on the fact that we made it out of the birthing experience with a healthy mother and new baby girl.

Chapter 12
A Message to the New Mother

"Sometimes the strength of motherhood
is greater than natural laws."

— Barbara Kingsolver

The joyous occasion of giving birth to Ericka's first child came face-to-face with her guilt of becoming a single parent. I reminded Ericka that she never set out to be a single parent. She gave birth to a child with a loving village supporting her every step of the way. It takes two to tango, and without a partner to dance with, you can participate freely in a line dance. Line dancing does not require a partner. Ericka welcomed the invitation to join the line dance of life and get on the floor with everyone who wanted to have fun. Our first fun event was the Zoom Sip and See. The Sip and See gathered people to sip the beverages, eat hors d'oeuvres, and visit the new mother and baby online.

Ericka, you and your baby are part of a village of well-wishers, friends, and loving family. Your IVF baby is our miracle. I thank God you had the support of the IVF girls during the pregnancy process.

Chapter 13
Sisterhood to Motherhood:
The Journey of the IVF Girls

Ericka's Story

"To have a friend, be a friend.
The only way to have a friend is to be one."

— Ralph Waldo Emerson

On November 2, 2019, Hannah created the group on Facebook at 8:48 PM. Hannah had two other ladies who also had their IVF embryos transferred message me on November 21, 2019. The initial questions we had for one another were, "Where is everyone from?" and "How many transfers have you had?" This questioning only made me feel more comfortable reaching out and becoming a part of this group of women. I finally had friends who got me. My girls. It all felt great to me because we were going through the same thing at the very same time! We were participating in the IVF process at the same time. They had husbands to support them in the process. I had them to be with me on this spiritual journey.

What a divine plan. I had new friends in a day and time when people didn't allow "new-new" into their circle of friends. I thought it was very lovely of Hannah to reach out to three strangers and forge our friendship. I felt blessed to be part of this sisterhood. One young lady who was part of the initial group had her transfer date moved to January due to her lining being trilaminar endometrium.[13] So, on November 16, she left the group. The three of us stayed in the group.

The group consisted of three of us: Hannah, 37 years old from Raleigh, North Carolina; Paris, 29 years old from Willis, Texas; and me, Ericka Michelle, 34 years old from Woodstock, Maryland. Three different women, three journeys, one mission: to make it through the IVF procedure successfully. These ladies were a godsend. It is the nonverbal understanding of the nervousness of the process that speaks volumes to our inner spirits. With the support and encouragement of my family, coworkers, and IVF girls, I finally had a village of people to help me make it through the conception and birthing process. The people who understand pregnancy from an IVF perspective are ready to give me

---

[13]According to fertility.igenomix.com, trilaminar endometrium refers to how "thick (or thin) your endometrium lining is and is an important factor for the implantation of your embryo, especially when you're going through the in vitro fertilization (IVF) process."

advice. The IVF girls and I kept each other informed of our doctors' appointments and our general IVF progress. Hannah and Paris had their embryo transfer on the same day; my transfer took place the next day. Hannah received her positive pregnancy test on November 25. Paris received her positive pregnancy test on November 27. I finally got a positive pregnancy test for the first time in my life on November 29th. The joy I felt goes far beyond the words on this page.

Determined to remain diligent about my first pregnancy, I took a pregnancy test every day for the entire first trimester. I was so afraid of losing my baby because I couldn't feel anything. However, I did experience an intense level of morning sickness but no movement of the baby. The daily pregnancy test gave me peace of mind. There were terrifying moments during the pregnancy. On January 24, I experienced heavy bleeding, so I went to the Emergency Department (ED). The ED doctor performed a sonogram, which showed that the baby was doing just fine. From my vantage point of the sonogram monitor, I saw my baby moving and singing in the womb with no care in the world. So, I did not need to worry. As scary as this was, I never knew until that day that some women bleed during pregnancy. My baby and I made it through that ordeal.

On a lighter note, the IVF girls and I humorously discussed our upcoming glucose tests. We gleefully compared notes as we strategized how to make it through that pregnancy phase together successfully. We made it. Ultimately, the most joyous occasion occurred when we all gave birth to our baby girls. Hannah and Paris gave birth on August 3, and I gave birth on August 13. Our IVF journey had some challenging times. However, the good times outweighed the bad times. I am extraordinarily blessed and grateful for my IVF girls. They supported me throughout my pregnancy every step of the way. Now my baby girl, Erielle, has an extended village bonded in sisterhood with the IVF girls.

Chapter 14
Doing Something Different

"The definition of insanity is doing the same thing
over and over and expecting different results."

— Albert Einstein

After the baby was born, the fork in the road loomed. Ericka pondered the questions: "Should I try to find love again? Should I get some pets? Should I become a cat lady? At that point in life, there was growing concern that Ericka simply did not have a proper formula for finding a soul mate." "Ericka, it is time to do something different if you decide to date again. You always have a type when picking a mate. The type has an attribute that doesn't necessarily make them good partners for a transparent, committed, loving relationship. Instead, you had partnered with others' private agendas that had nothing to do with you. I want to suggest that you allow me to take on the role of your life coach. Allow me to walk you through the dating process with you," I said. I figured if both of us, along with Ericka's therapist, assisted her in identifying "red flags" in men, maybe the chance for getting into a successful relationship would prevail.

Ericka was open to allowing us to work with her on managing her dating life. Living in a home with her father and me gave us real-time access to Ericka's friendships while she continued weekly sessions with her therapist. From my perspective, Ericka's therapist is a Godsend who helped Ericka get in touch with her feelings. The reflective aspect of the therapy sessions afforded Ericka a deeper understanding of how a toxic relationship impacts mental health. Ericka learned from her therapist not to get sucked into acting in a manner outside of her character. The loving self-first rule commands Ericka's actions in this phase of life. When dating starts, there are rules of engagement.

The rules for engagement in the dating process are straightforward. First, stay away from anyone in a stated profession (we won't say here) because Ericka attracts the leeches from that profession, meaning she attracts those who see her as their way out of their life's circumstances rather than see themselves as providers. Please believe, we are well aware that not all people in that profession are like that; some are beautiful providers. She needs to avoid that type. Second, eliminate standard physical attributes as a mandate. Meet the person to determine if there is chemistry. Third, the person must celebrate and not tolerate her. Fourth, the person must not try to separate Ericka from having a relationship with her parents. Last, they must have pictures posted on social media that show their eyes since the eyes are windows to the soul.

Lessons learned from dating:

Momma's boy, who failed to take his meds: Threatened Ericka with bodily harm when she could not loan him $250.

Drug dealer and pimp: Met him at the mall. He was about "growth love and not broke love." He requested she give him $2,500 to hold in an envelope "for safekeeping."

A person who thought highly of himself: Dates video vixens and is used to women falling all over him.

Unkept pastor: A sloppy, very large pastor, deep in debt, who barely worked looking for someone to help him out of his situation.

The frat brother/teacher: His action and words didn't align. He appeared to be an all-around good guy yet expects women to fall out over the chance to be part of his frat room lifestyles.

Disconnected politician: He wanted a relationship without putting any effort to make the connection happen.

Single father, very kind and broken: Fresh out of a very toxic marriage and carried the weight of the world on his shoulders. He will make a great husband for someone one day.

I met my match with a handsome hustler/provider: He showed love daily through words, actions, and deeds. However, he refused to commit to being in a relationship. Unfortunately, Ericka could no longer waste time in a one-sided relationship with all love and respect due to a charming person. Now, they are not in a relationship because Ericka moved on.

Ericka learned when dating, words and actions must match. Don't treat her like a wife if you are not in a relationship. When in a relationship, both parties must give the relationship a title. Once the "red flag" showed itself to Ericka, the following Dear John Letter ensued.

Dear (Insert the name),

Nice meeting you; however, I am not interested in getting to know you further. I wish you the best in your pursuit of happiness in life and love. Have a wonderful day. –

Ericka's dating lessons taught her to go through the weeds to get the flowers. Follow Dr. Maya Angelou's philosophy: "When someone shows you who they are, believe them the first time." Before beginning the dating process, everyone should read an article like *11 Signs You're Dating a Narcissist — and How to Get Out,* written by Gabrielle Kassel — Updated on January 30, 2019, https://www.healthline.com/health/mental-health/am-i-dating-a-narcissist.

Chapter 15
Ericka's Closing Words

I had weight loss surgery and several fertility procedures to include one successful IVF attempt throughout this process. As a life partner with someone who exhibited the characteristics of a narcissist, I did not have a fan club within my marriage residence when I got a positive pregnancy test. Leaving the marriage residence to start over again was my destiny with no options. A divorcee and single parent are the titles I carried throughout my pregnancy. After childbirth, I struggled to lose weight and had to learn to date in the world of social media. I also had to learn to love myself truly.

My new normal is the mandate to start looking into the mirror and like what I see, laugh out loud, and whip my hair back and forth with joy. I learned not to allow someone's inability to be vulnerable, laugh, and experience life's fun to preclude me from receiving the love I truly deserve. I will make sure the person I love is emphatic with an ability to celebrate with others. I vow to make sure my future life partner has long-term friends and engages with people as his authentic self. If the person doesn't acknowledge our relationship publicly, I won't entertain him privately. I will head for the hills and not look back. I will run!

We hope this book offers information to help you understand the complexities of toxic relationships that may impact your IVF journey or your life in general. I realized that just because a person appears to be one way in public does not mean that's who they are in private. In other words, a public smile can unleash personal aggression. And if you're not careful of people around you, you can think you're the problem. Know the red flags when someone attacks you with a complex story you shared with them. For example, if you shared a story about past hurts and they later say, "I know why they hurt you." That is an example of using your account against you. That's a red flag!

When trouble arises in your relationship, allow a therapist to help you understand *why* you behave the way you did in a given situation. The therapist will put language to the behavior you have that appears to be disjointed by the outsider. The therapist will get you in touch with who you are and teach you how to do self-care. The life coach helps you with the day-to-day instructions on *moving forward and navigating* this sometimes-cruel world. Do not be hard on yourself if you don't know how to move without help.

Remember, you don't know all there is to know. Until you know what you don't know, you can't feel guilty because there was no way of knowing the unknown.

Thank you...

Thank you, Mommy, for creatively and gracefully telling my story! I appreciate you for being with me during this entire journey. Thank you for all your prayers, middle-of-the-night rescues, and for being an awesome Big Momma to Itty Bitty! I appreciate and love you forever and always,

— Ericka Michelle